play guitar with...

cream

CW00664009

Wise Publications
part of The Music Sales Group
London / New York / Paris / Sydney / Copenhagen / Berlin / Madrid / Tokyo

Published by
Wise Publications
8/9 Frith Street,
London W1D 3JB, England

Exclusive Distributors:
Music Sales Limited
Distribution Centre, Newmarket Road,
Bury St Edmunds, Suffolk IP33 3YB
Music Sales Pty Limited
120 Rothschild Avenue,
Rosebery, NSW 2018, Australia

Order No. AM982894
ISBN 1-84609-062-8
This book © Copyright 2005 Wise Publications,
a division of Music Sales Limited.

Compiled by Nick Crispin
Music arranged by Arthur Dick
Music processed by Paul Ewers Music Design
Cover designed by Fresh Lemon
Cover photograph courtesy of Dezo Hoffmann/Rex Features
Printed in the United Kingdom by
Caligraving Limited, Thetford, Norfolk

CD recorded, mixed and mastered by Jonas Persson
All guitars by Arthur Dick
Bass by Paul Townsend
Drums by Brett Morgan
Harmonica by Stuart Constable

Your Guarantee of Quality

As publishers, we strive to produce
every book to the highest commercial standards.
The music has been freshly engraved and the book has
been carefully designed to minimise awkward page turns
and to make playing from it a real pleasure.
Particular care has been given to specifying acid-free,
neutral-sized paper made from pulps which have not been
elemental chlorine bleached. This pulp is from farmed
sustainable forests and was produced with
special regard for the environment.
Throughout, the printing and binding have been planned
to ensure a sturdy, attractive publication which
should give years of enjoyment.
If your copy fails to meet our high standards,
please inform us and we will gladly replace it.

www.musicsales.com

badge

Words & Music by Eric Clapton & George Harrison

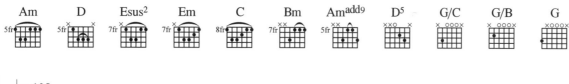

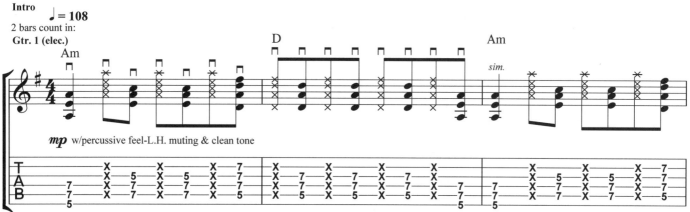

Play written part throughout

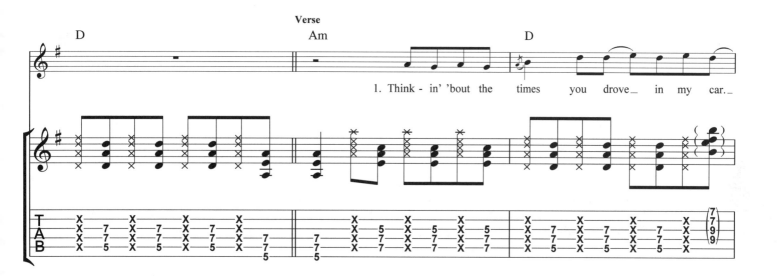

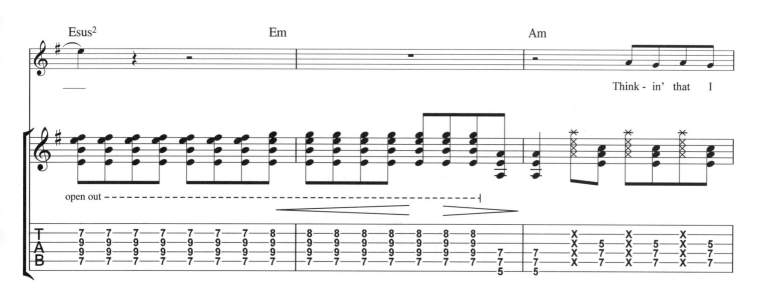

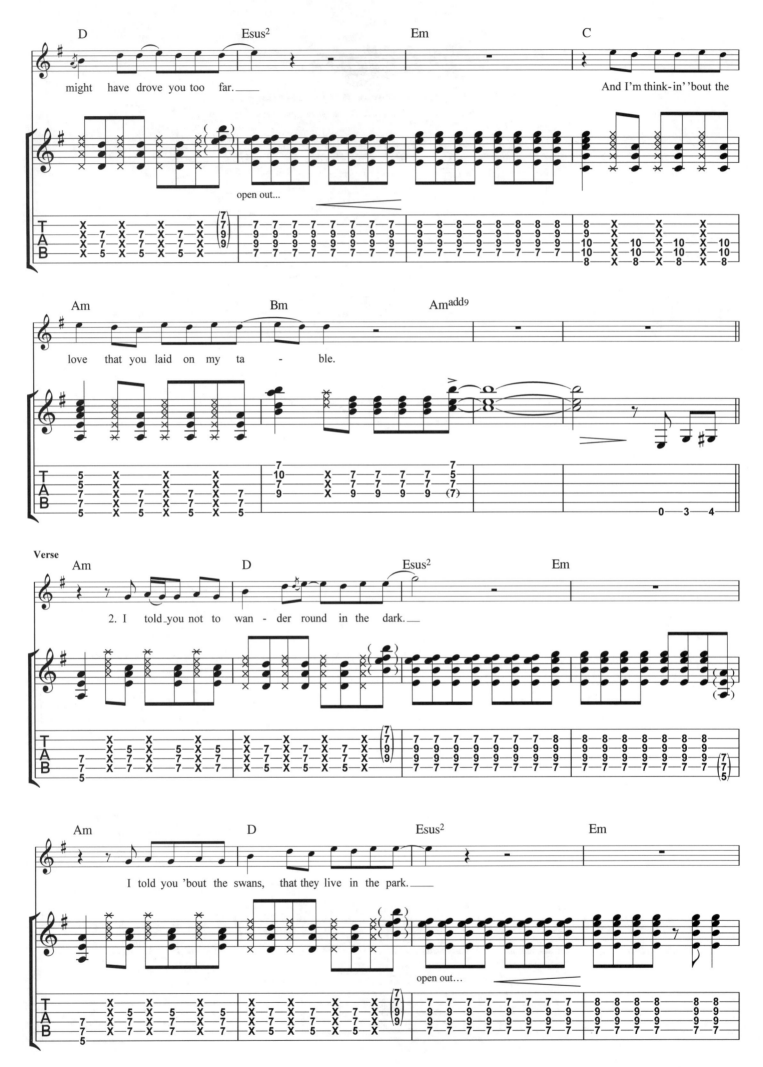

4

Yes be - fore__they bring the cur - tain down.__ Wooh,__ ooh. ___

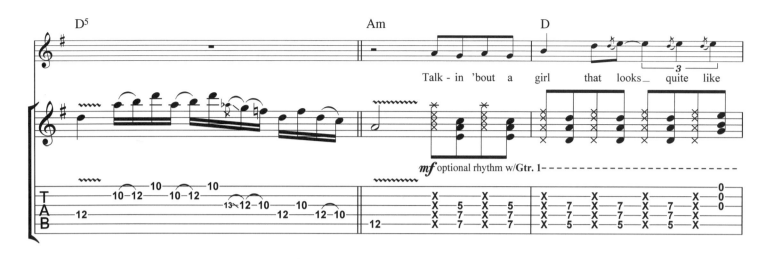

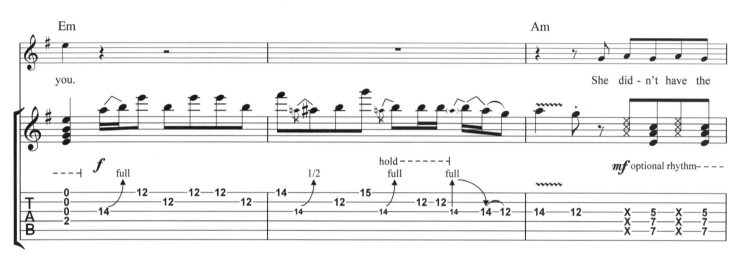

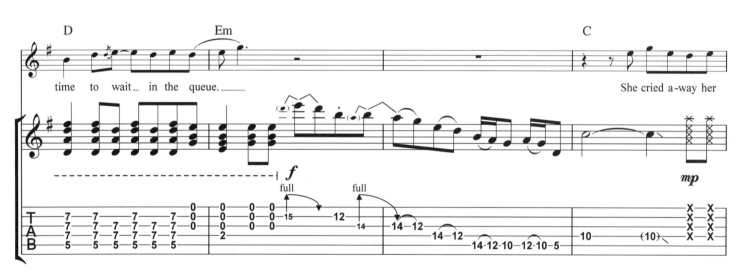

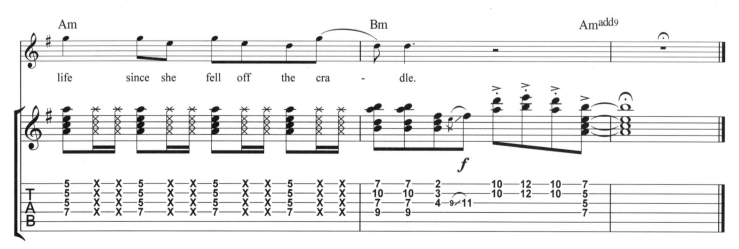

crossroads

Words & Music by Robert Johnson
arranged by Eric Clapton

Intro
2 bars count in:

♩=132

*chords implied by harmony

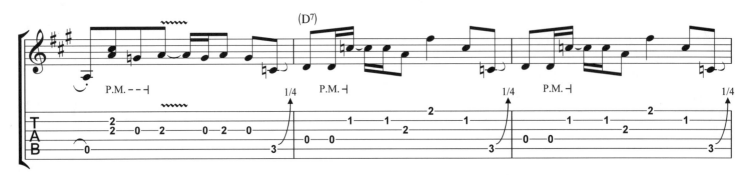

1. I went down

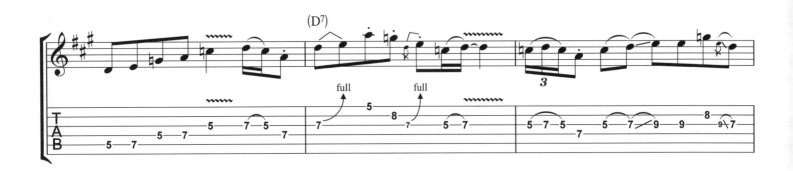

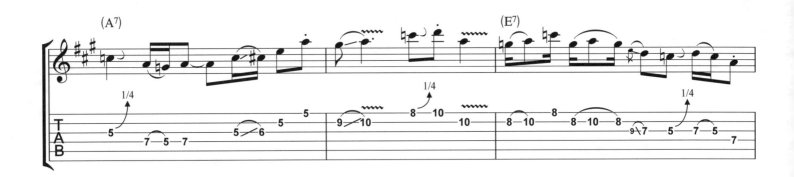

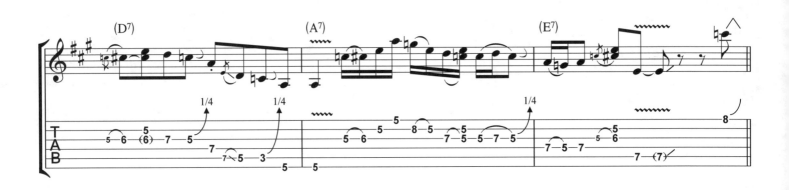

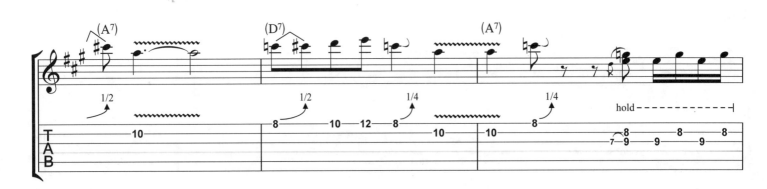

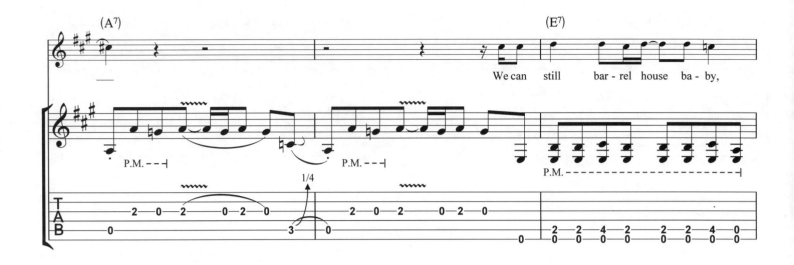

We can still bar - rel house ba - by,

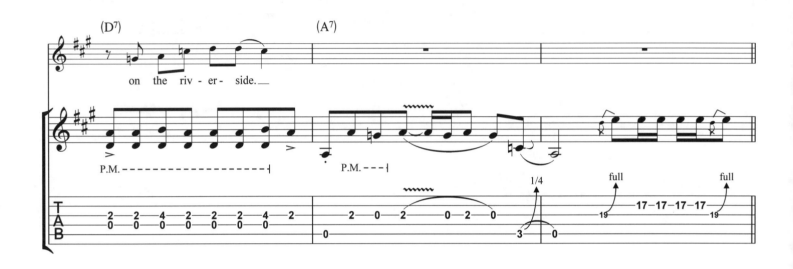

on the riv - er - side.

Solo

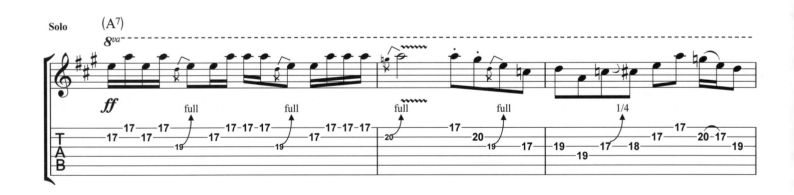

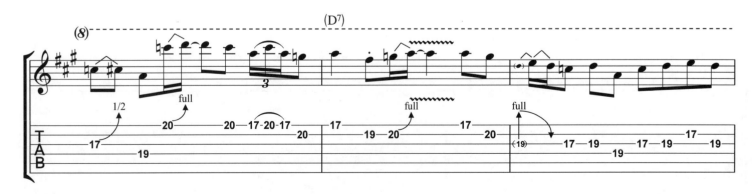

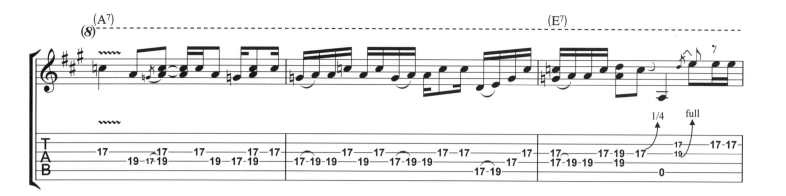

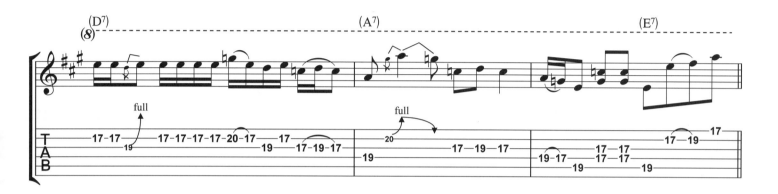

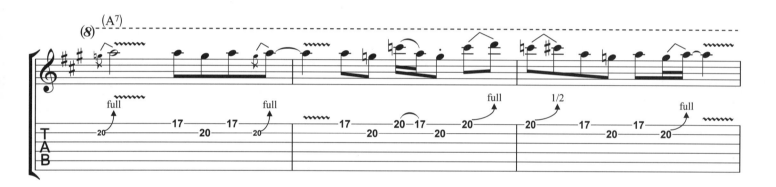

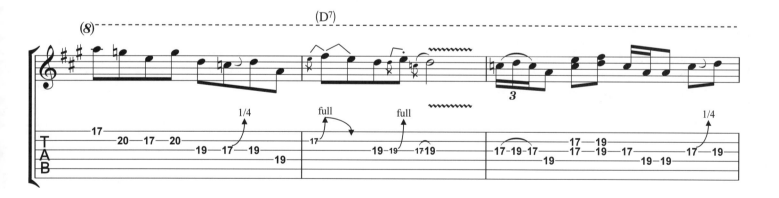

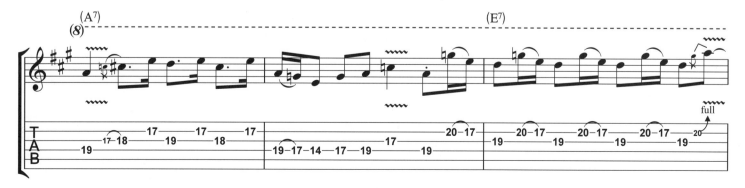

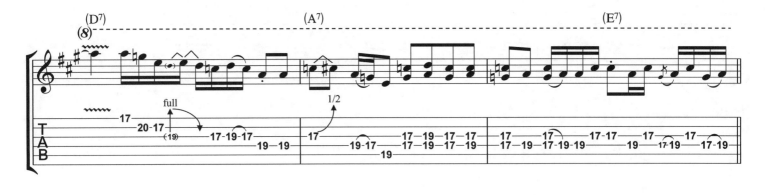

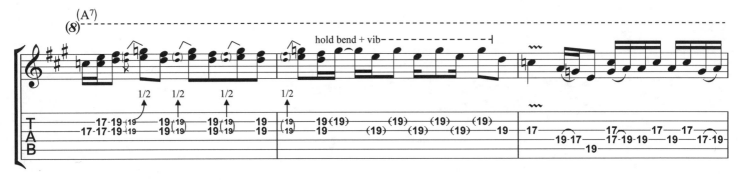

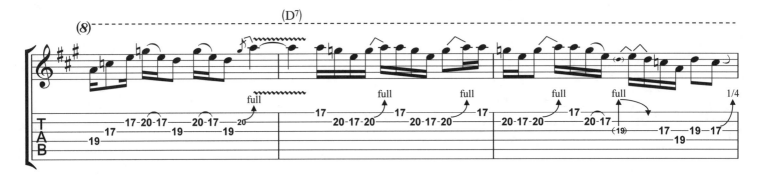

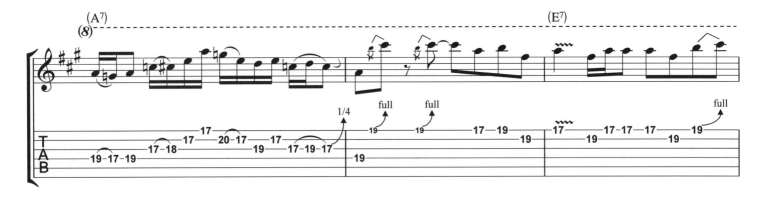

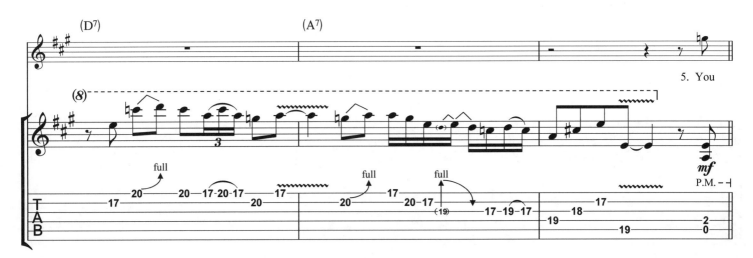

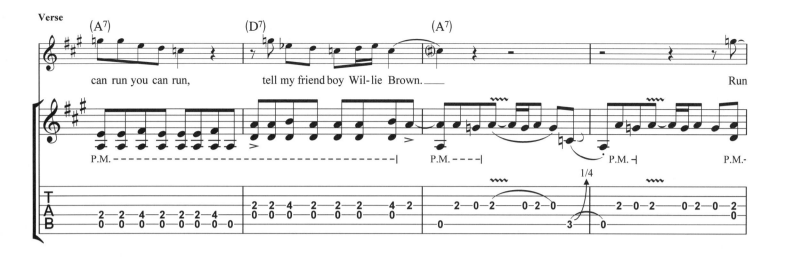

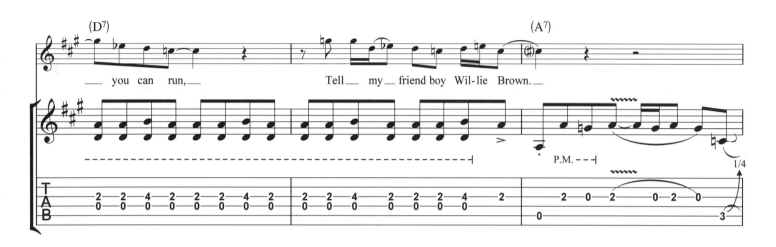

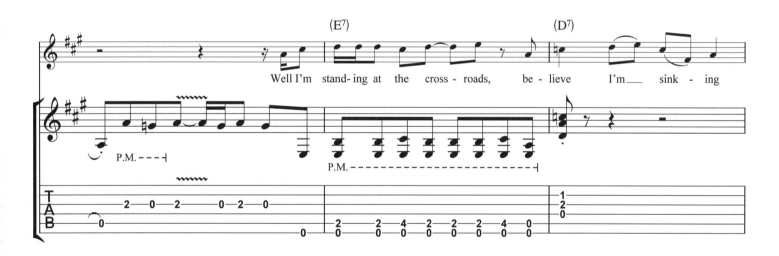

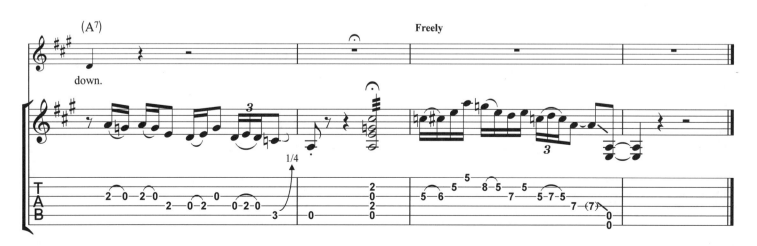

15

spoonful

Words & Music by Willie Dixon

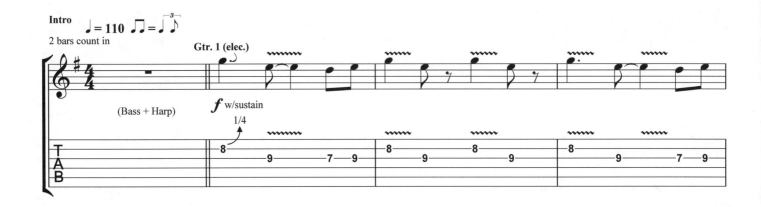

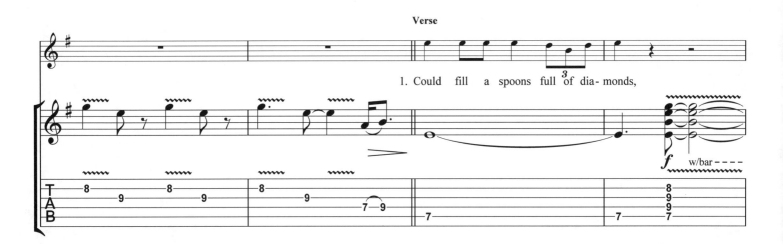

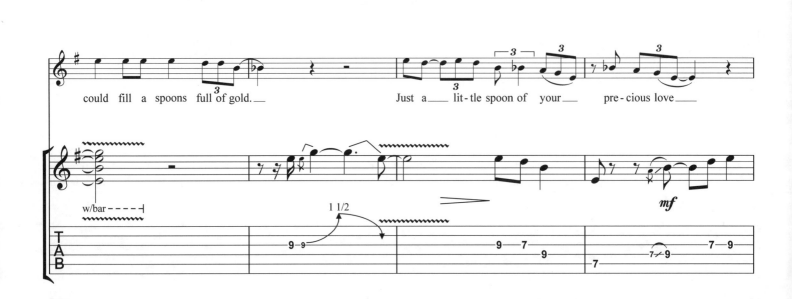

spoon, that spoon, that spoon - ful.___ That spoon, that spoon, that spoon.

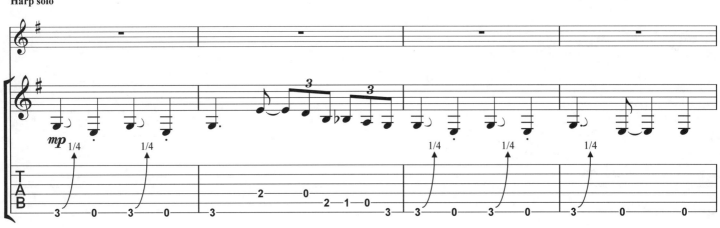

Harp solo

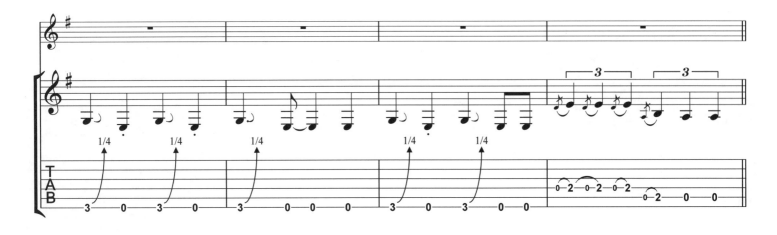

Verse

2. Could fill a spoons full of cof - fee; could fill a spoons full of tea.___

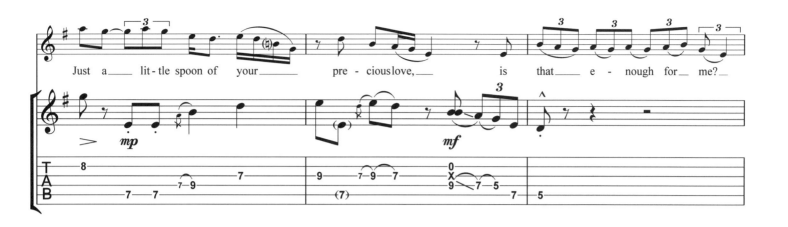

Just a___ lit-tle spoon of your___ pre-cious love,___ is that___ e-nough for__ me?__

Men_____ lies_____ a-bout it.   Some of them

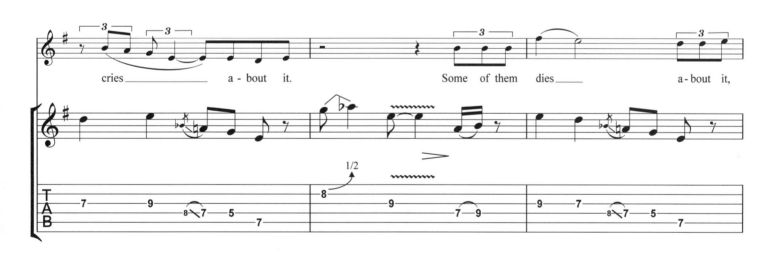

cries_____ a-bout it.   Some of them dies_____ a-bout it,

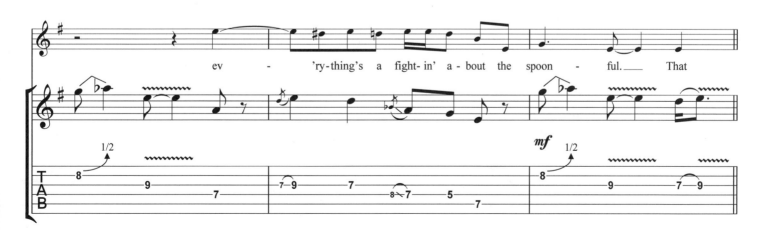

ev - 'ry-thing's a fight-in' a-bout the spoon - ful.__ That

Solo

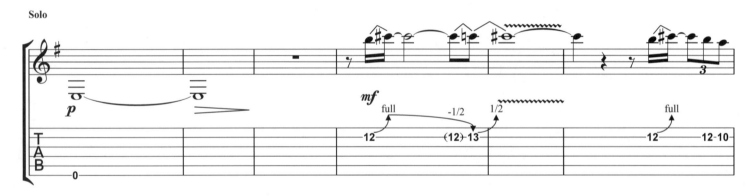

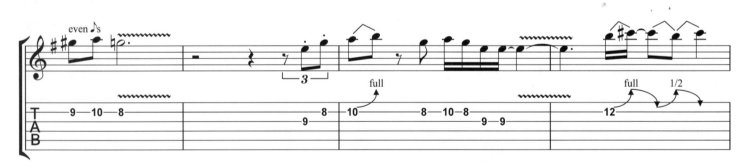

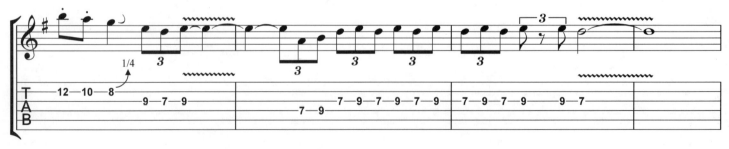

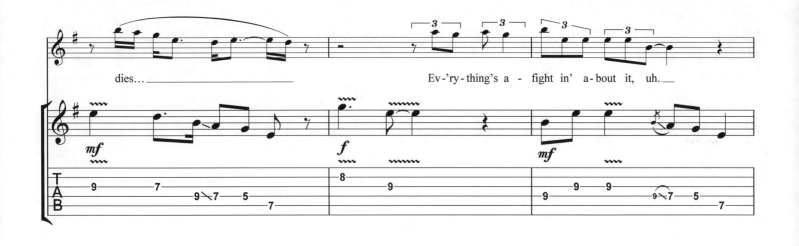

dies... Ev-'ry-thing's a - fight in' a-bout it, uh.

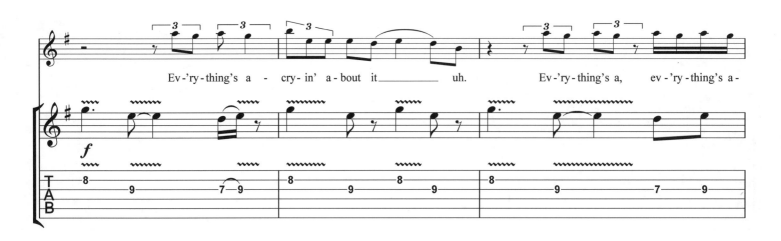

Ev-'ry-thing's a - cry-in' a-bout it_____ uh. Ev-'ry-thing's a, ev-'ry-thing's a-

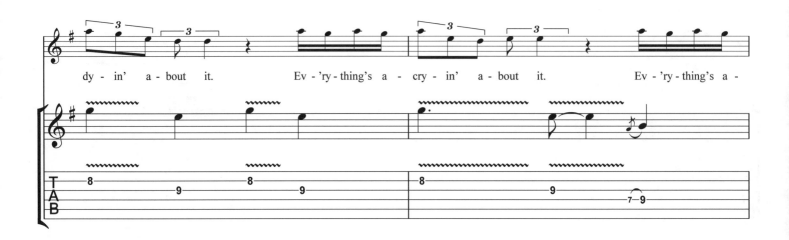

dy-in' a-bout it. Ev-'ry-thing's a - cry-in' a-bout it. Ev-'ry-thing's a-

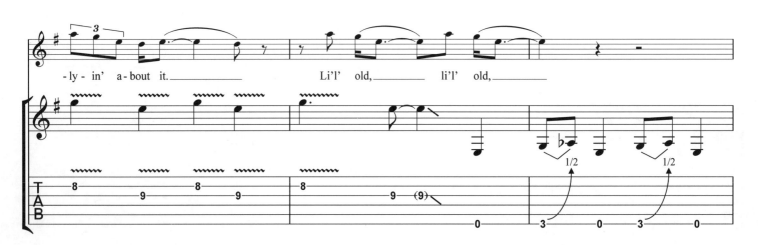

-ly-in' a-bout it._____ Li'l old,_____ li'l old,_____

spoon, lit-tle old spoon, lit-tle old spoon - ful.__ That spoon, that spoon, that spoon - ful.__

Spoon, that spoon, that spoon - ful.__ Yeah._____

*Ev-'ry-thing's a-dy-in' a-bout it.__   Hey!_____

*Vocal line cued on track by gtr.

strange brew

Words & Music by Eric Clapton, Gail Collins & Felix Pappalardi

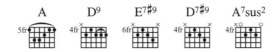

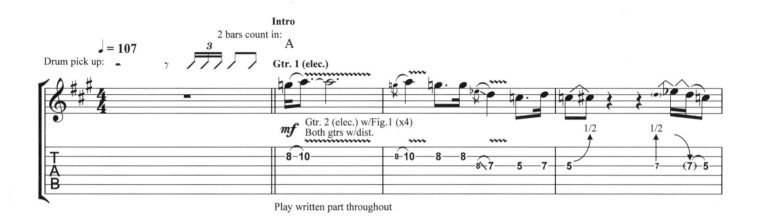

Play written part throughout

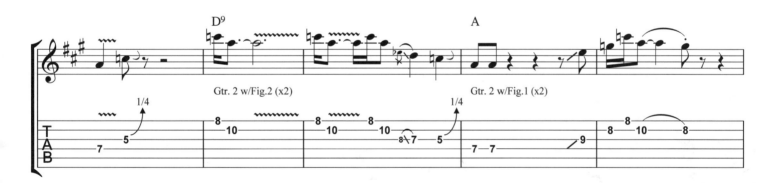

Strange___ brew, kill-in' what's in - side___ of you. _____ 1. She's a

don't watch out_ it - 'll stick to you, to you._ What kind of fool are you?

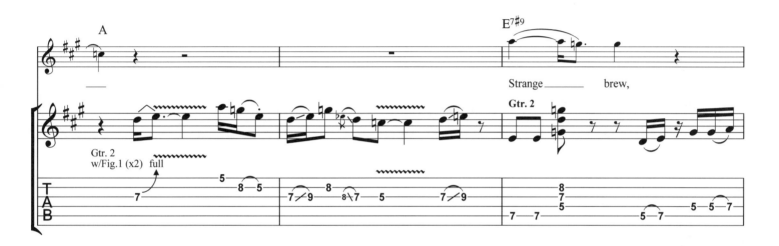

Strange_ brew,

kill-in' what's in - side_ of you._

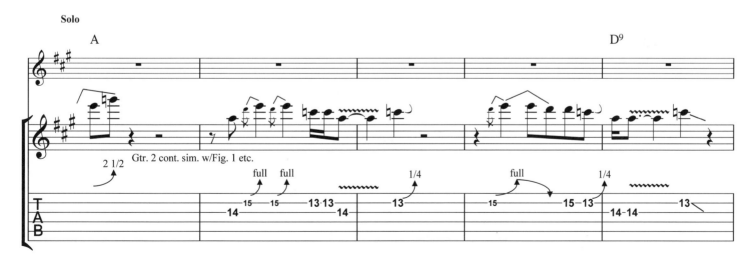

Solo

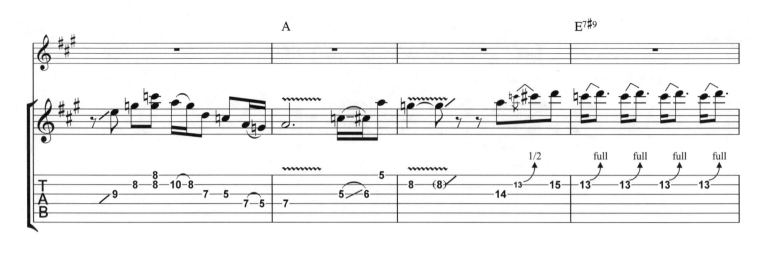

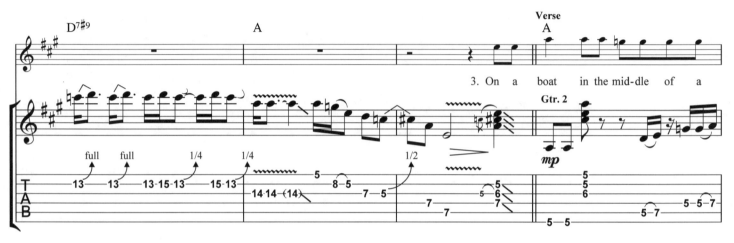

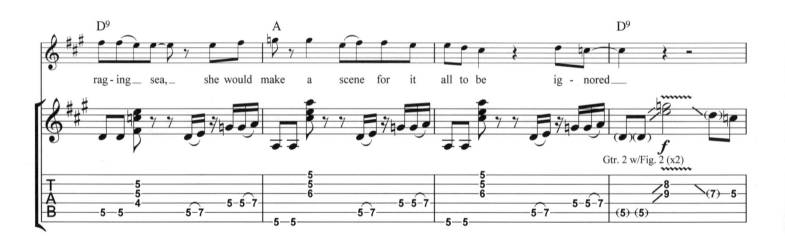

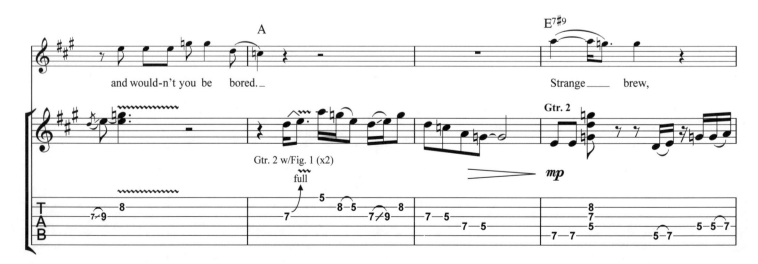

sunshine of your love

Words & Music by Jack Bruce, Pete Brown & Eric Clapton

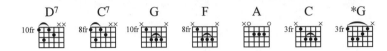

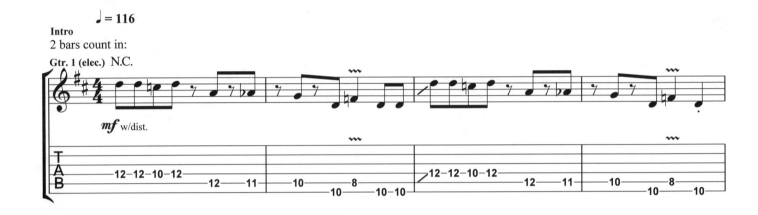

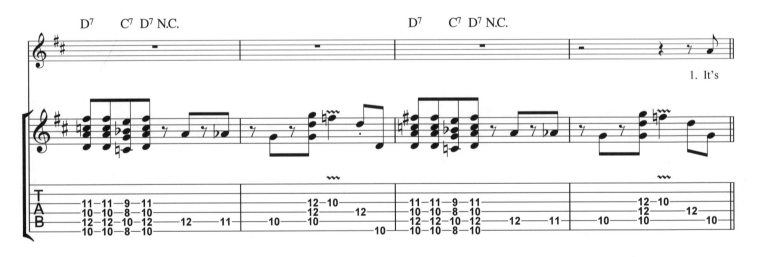

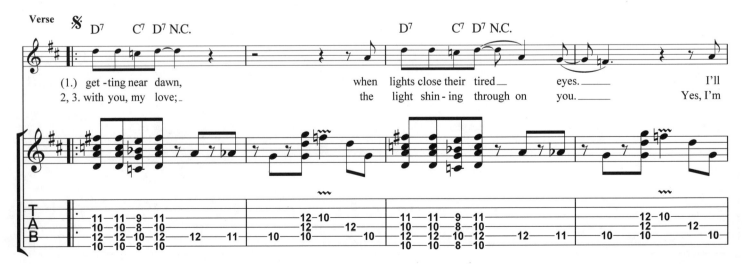

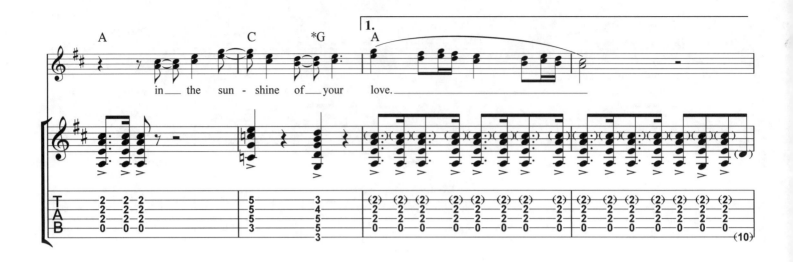

in— the sun - shine of—your love.

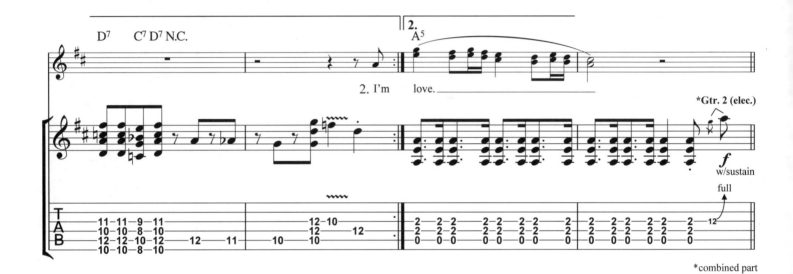

2. I'm love.—

*combined part

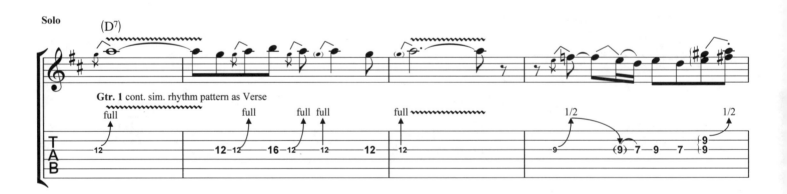

Gtr. 1 cont. sim. rhythm pattern as Verse

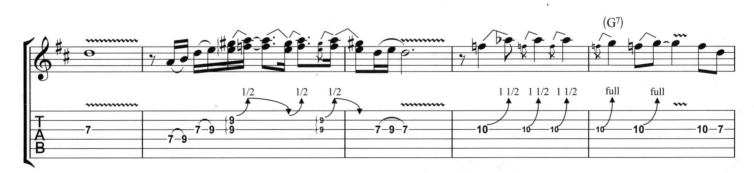

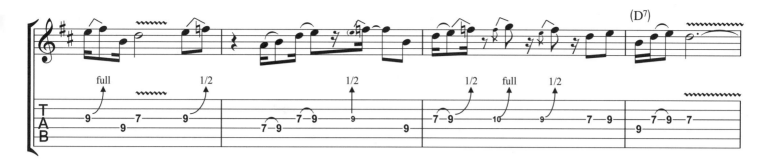

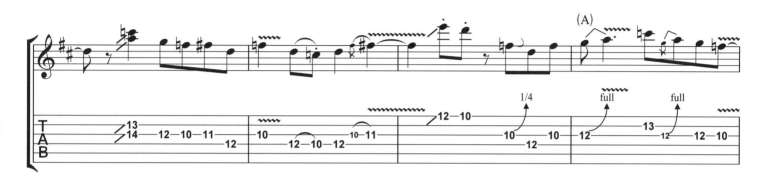

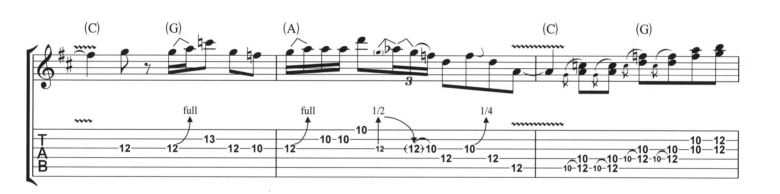

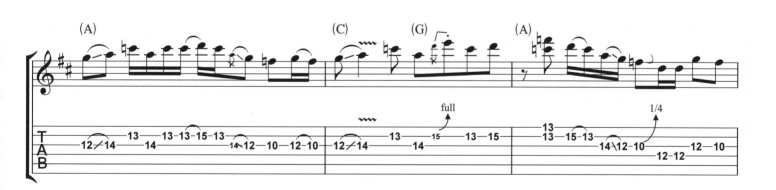

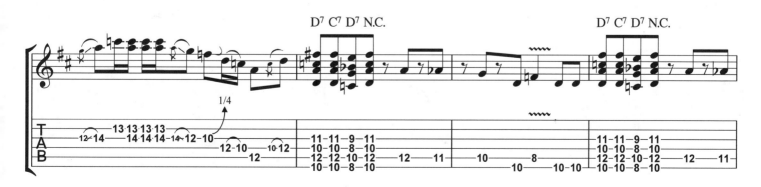

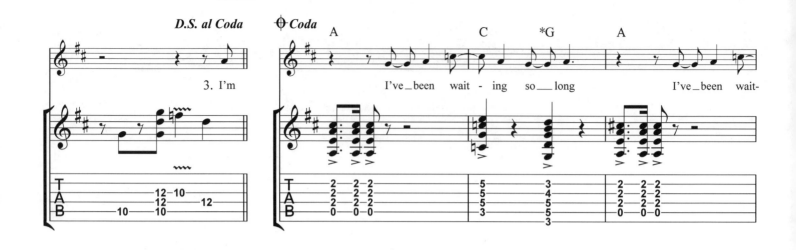

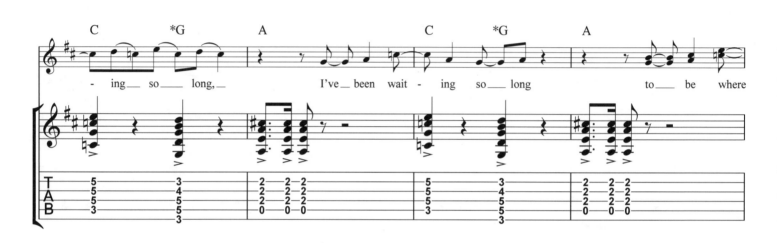

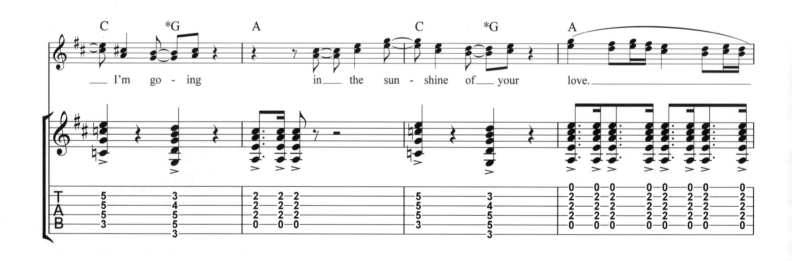

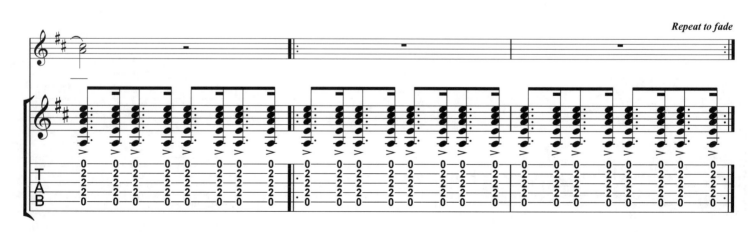

tales of brave ulysses

Words & Music by Eric Clapton & Martin Sharp

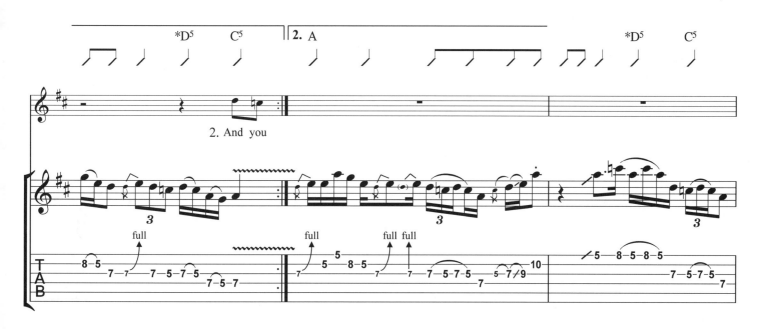

laugh-ing through your fin - gers, and you want to take her with you to the hard land of the win-ter.

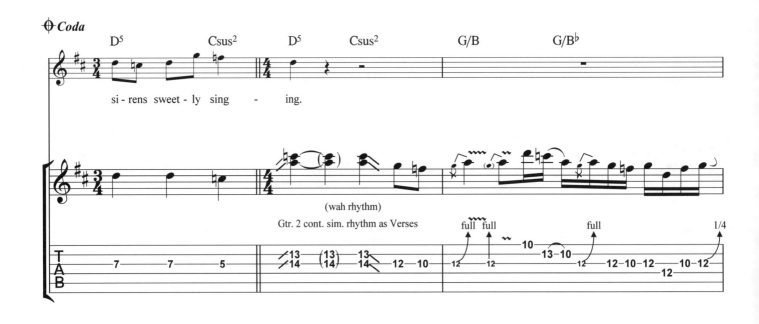

si - rens sweet - ly sing - ing.

(wah rhythm)
Gtr. 2 cont. sim. rhythm as Verses

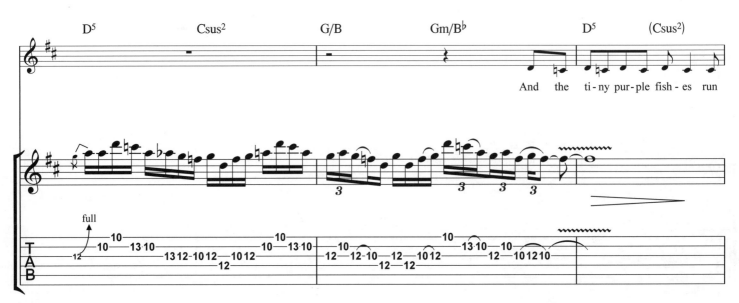

And the ti - ny pur-ple fish - es run

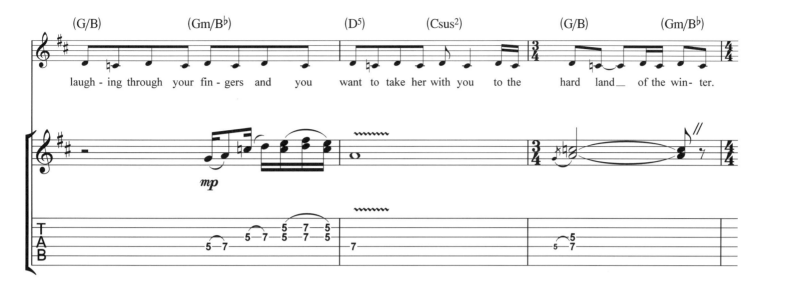

laugh - ing through your fin - gers and you want to take her with you to the hard land__ of the win - ter.

Outro

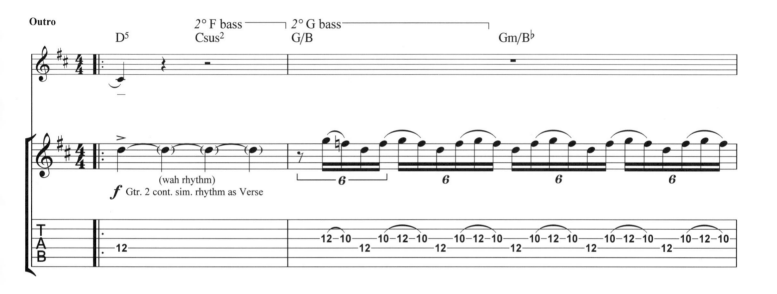

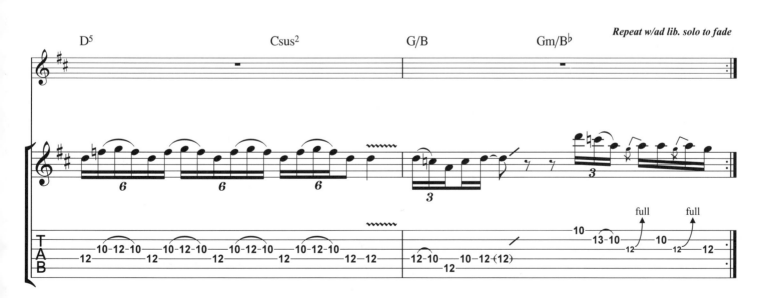

white room

Words & Music by Jack Bruce & Pete Brown

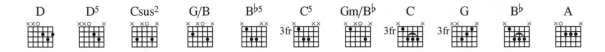

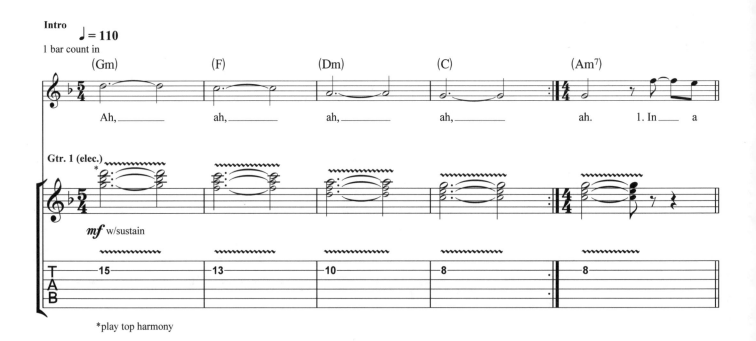

*play top harmony

44

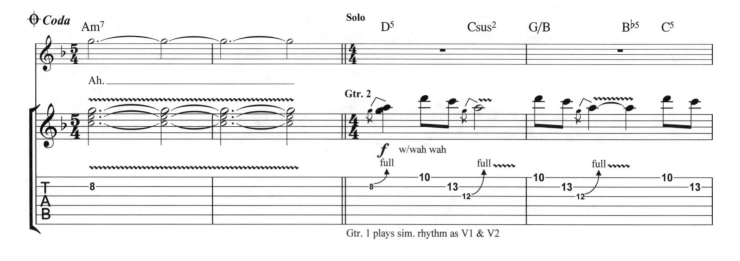

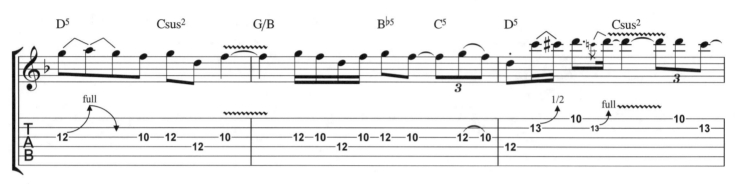

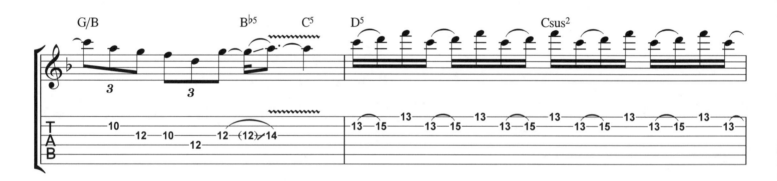

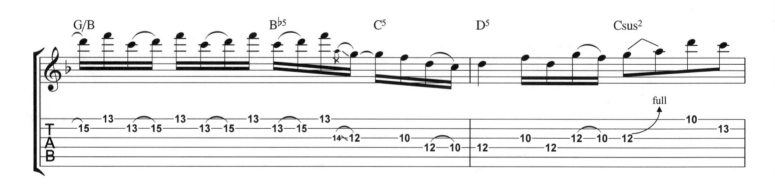

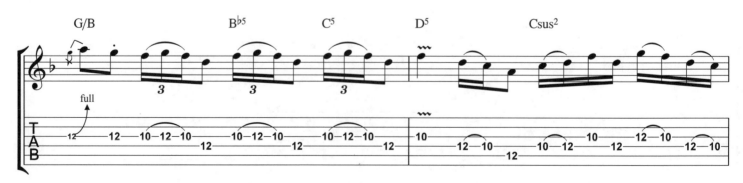

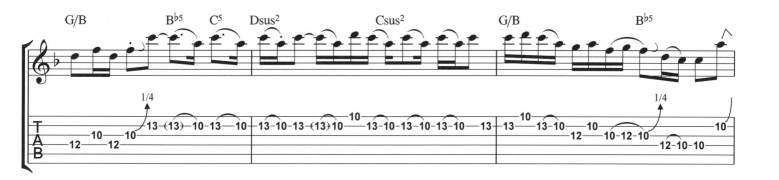

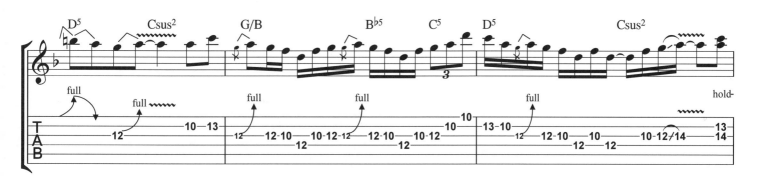

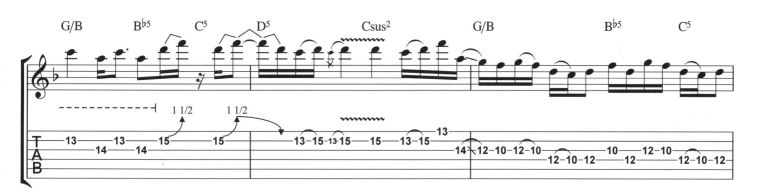

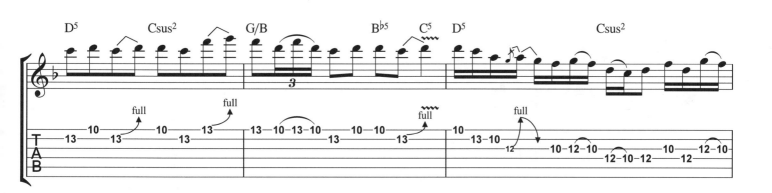

Repeat ad lib. to fade

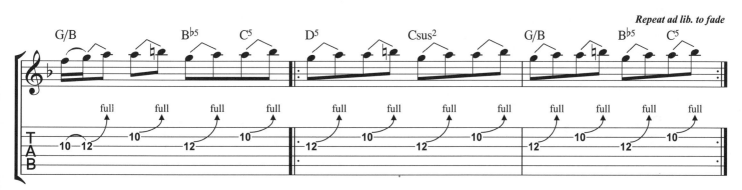

guitar tablature explained

Guitar music be notated in three different ways: on a musical stave, in tablature, and in rhythm slashes.

RHYTHM SLASHES are written above the stave. Strum chords in the rhythm indicated. Round noteheads indicate single notes.

THE MUSICAL STAVE shows pitches and rhythms and is divided by lines into bars. Pitches are named after the first seven letters of the alphabet.

TABLATURE graphically represents the guitar fingerboard. Each horizontal line represents a string, and each number represents a fret.

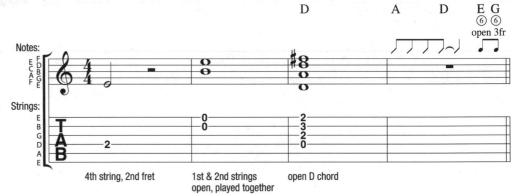

4th string, 2nd fret

1st & 2nd strings open, played together

open D chord

definitions for special guitar notation

SEMI-TONE BEND: Strike the note and bend up a semi-tone (1/2 step).

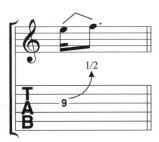

WHOLE-TONE BEND: Strike the note and bend up a whole-tone (whole step).

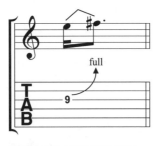

GRACE NOTE BEND: Strike the note and bend as indicated. Play the first note as quickly as possible.

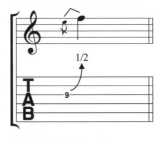

QUARTER-TONE BEND: Strike the note and bend up a 1/4 step.

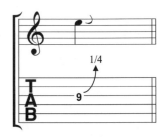

BEND & RELEASE: Strike the note and bend up as indicated, then release back to the original note.

COMPOUND BEND & RELEASE: Strike the note and bend up and down in the rhythm indicated.

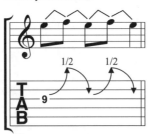

PRE-BEND: Bend the note as indicated, then strike it.

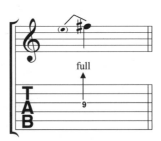

PRE-BEND & RELEASE: Bend the note as indicated. Strike it and release the note back to the original pitch.

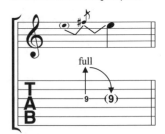

HAMMER-ON: Strike the first note with one finger, then sound the second note (on the same string) with another finger by fretting it without picking.

PULL-OFF: Place both fingers on the notes to be sounded, strike the first note and without picking, pull the finger off to sound the second note.

LEGATO SLIDE (GLISS): Strike the first note and then slide the same fret-hand finger up or down to the second note. The second note is not struck.

MUFFLED STRINGS: A percussive sound is produced by laying the fret hand across the string(s) without depressing, and striking them with the pick hand.

NATURAL HARMONIC: Strike the note while the fret-hand lightly touches the string directly over the fret indicated.

PICK SCRAPE: The edge of the pick is rubbed down (or up) the string, producing a scratchy sound.

PALM MUTING: The note is partially muted by the pick hand lightly touching the string(s) just before the bridge.

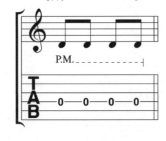

SHIFT SLIDE (GLISS & RESTRIKE): Same as legato slide, except the second note is struck.

1 2 3 4 5 6 7 8 9

NOTE: The speed of any bend is indicated by the music notation and tempo.